A Night in Space

by Edenbridge, Tonbridge and Tunbridge Wells book club members
illustrated by Beth Aulton

Beyond Words

London

First edition published 2016 by Books Beyond Words.

Text & illustrations © Books Beyond Words 2016.

No part of this book may be reproduced in any form, or by any means without prior permission in writing from the publisher.

ISBN 978-1-78458-081-0

British Library Cataloguing-in-Publication Data
A catalogue record for this book is available from the British Library.

Printed by Book Printing UK, Peterborough.

Books Beyond Words is a Community Interest Company registered in England and Wales (7557861).

St George's Hospital Charity is a registered charity (no. 241527).

Contents

Storyline

The following words are provided for readers and supporters who want some ideas about one possible story. Most readers make their own story up from the pictures.

1. Annie loves outer space. She dreams about flying through space to another planet.

2. On the planet, Annie meets a big, green alien.

3. Annie and the alien sing and dance together.

4. A rocket flies towards the planet.

5. The rocket lands and three space explorers come out. Annie says hello.

6. Annie helps the space explorers set up their camp.

7. They all relax around the campfire. Annie dances to the music. A big, green hand appears...

8. It's the alien! He wants to join the dancing. But the space explorers think Annie is in danger.

9. The space explorers make lots of noise to scare away the alien. Annie tells them to stop. The alien is her friend.

10. Annie and the space explorers comfort the alien. The space explorers are sorry for scaring him.

11. The space explorer shows the alien a picture of a star. They need to find stars to take home with them. Can the alien help them?

12. The alien pokes the campfire and stars come out.

18

13. Annie and the space explorers collect as many stars as they can to take home.

14. Annie says goodbye to the friends in her dream.

15. In the morning, Annie remembers her dream. She feels happy.

Pictures to colour for yourself

You can bring your own artistic talents to the story and colour some of the pictures for yourself on the next pages.

Felt tips work best for colouring these pictures.

Picture This

Valuing individual creativity is very important to our sense of well-being. This idea was at the centre of everything we did in this project and helped bring out the best in all of us.

Kent libraries in partnership with Beyond Words worked with self-advocates and artists to develop three innovative picture books. The storylines were developed through a series of drama workshops with self-advocates engaging in a story making process. Using drama to improvise scenes and develop stories for the artists to capture, we created three original picture books for people with learning disabilities.

Beyond Words' project team made 15 visits to nine Kent book clubs, holding drama workshops to invent the original stories. The artists drew the first set of pictures based on the drama sessions, and self-advocates then read and commented on them. The pictures were edited and redrawn in response to the feedback from the book clubs and readers in local day centres and activity groups.

Trialling the pictures several times across multiple visits to book clubs helped the artists to make the stories as clear and engaging as possible. Honouring the opinions and choices of people on the project has kept the book club readers' voices genuinely at the centre of the stories.

There has been a lot of laughter on this project and people have told us how much they have enjoyed taking part.

Related titles

A Balloon Adventure (2016) by Dartford, Maidstone and Sittingbourne book clubs, illustrated by Gaby Weigert. Stuart and Zoe are going on holiday in their hot air balloon. A gust of wind catches them by surprise, but with a bit of help the pair are soon back on track. Their trip ends up being a much bigger adventure than they had expected.

A Day at the Beach (2016) by Deal, Dover and Folkestone book clubs, illustrated by Lucy Bergonzi. Friends Ellie, Nadya, Miles and Rob are spending a day at the seaside. They have fun swimming, building sandcastles, eating ice cream and subathing. But the friends soon meet a seagull determined to cause mischief.

Ginger is a Hero (2015) by Beth Webb. Mary and her neighbour Mrs Hill don't get on. Mrs Hill gets really cross when her cat, Ginger, makes friends with Mary. But when Mrs Hill collapses at home, it's down to Mary and Ginger to save her life.

Beyond Words

To find out more about Beyond Words training and publications please visit our website: www.booksbeyondwords.co.uk

Artist

Beth Aulton has worked as a freelance Illustrator for a number of years. She studied Visual Communication, specialising in Illustration (BA Hons) at Birmingham City University followed by an art based prostgraduate qualification at Reading University. Her illustration work combines ink, paint and often collage with digital media. Beth's website is www.bethaulton.com

Acknowledgments

A big thank you to the three book clubs who created the story. The Library Ladies at Edenbridge: Jane, Pamela, Christine, Winnie and supporters Kim and Jill. Tonbridge book club: Jessica, Joanna, David, Rosemary, Georgina, Joel, Simon, Nigel and supporters Terry, Kelly, Jo and Pam. Tunbridge Wells Book Worms: Eric, Kevin, Anne, Edward, Nicky and supporter Sue.

Special thanks to Liz Taylor from Kent Libraries for her tireless support and for the initial idea that inspired this whole project.

Thank you to the book clubs, groups and day services who trialled the pictures: Everyday English Group Sittingbourne, Skillnet Catering Group and Independent Living Skill Group Tunbridge Wells.

We are grateful to Arts Council England for their generous funding of this project.

How to read this book

There is no right or wrong way to read this book. Remember it is not necessary to be able to read the words.

1. Some people are not used to reading books. Start at the beginning and read the story in each picture. Encourage the reader to hold the book themselves and to turn the pages at their own pace.

2. Whether you are reading the book with one person or with a group, encourage them to tell the story in their own words. You may think something different is happening in the pictures yourself, but that doesn't matter. Don't challenge the reader(s) or suggest their ideas are wrong.

3. You can help readers along by asking questions like:
- Who do you think that is?
- What is happening?
- How is he or she feeling?
- Do you ever feel like that?

4. You don't have to read the whole book in one sitting. Have fun with it: allow people time to chat about what they are reading and to follow the pictures at their own pace.

5. You can use the pictures as a storyboard for a drama group to create a play of the book.